Wind Rocket

by Chris Parker
Illustrated by Emma Levey

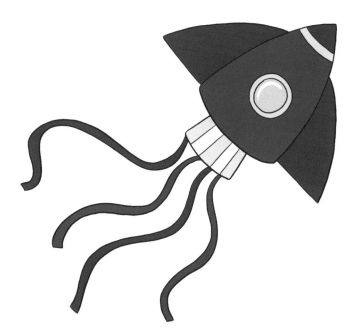

OXFORD

UNIVERSITY PRESS

In this book ...

Pip

Kit

Pip and Kit help get lost things back.

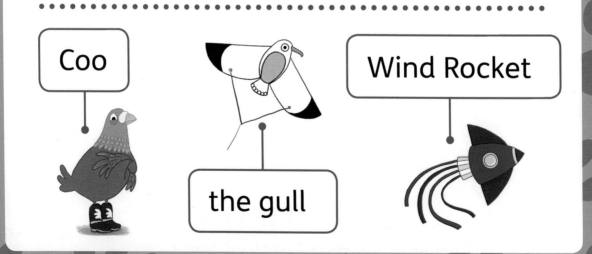

Coo

the gull

Wind Rocket

Pip and Kit were in the park.

Get the gull to go higher, Pip!

Look at the trees in the picture. They have <u>bare</u> branches, without any leaves. What time of year do you think it is?

3

Just then, a yell rang out.

Wind Rocket went higher and higher.

Just then, Coo shot down. He got the string and shot off ... with Wind Rocket!

"We must get Wind Rocket back," Pip said.
Pip and Kit started to run.

Coo was at the top of the hill.

Pip and Kit hid in the shrubs.

Pip and Kit are hiding <u>among</u> the shrubs. Does that mean they are a little way off from the shrubs or right inside them?

"Quick, Kit!" said Pip. "Send the gull up! Coo will get a shock."

Pip has decided to use the gull kite to help them.
Do you think Pip has made the right <u>decision</u>?
What <u>decision</u> would you make if you were Pip?

The gull went high. Pip kept a tight grip on the string.

"A gull!" Coo said, with a gulp.
He let go of his string and shot off.

Does Coo think the gull is <u>friendly</u>? Which words in the text tell you how he is feeling?

Kit got up on the bench.

I will get
Wind Rocket!

This is the <u>final</u> part of the plan to get the kite back.
Can you remember all of the other parts of the plan?

Pip and Kit took Wind Rocket back.
They left it on a bench.

The boy thought that Wind Rocket was lost <u>forever</u>.
Does that mean he thought he would get the kite back,
or not?

Retell the story

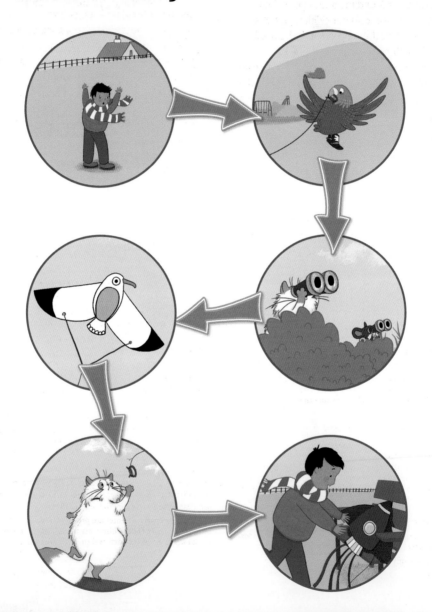